TERENCE GREAVES

SWINGING RHYMES

TEN PIECES IN POPULAR STYLES

THE ASSOCIATED BOARD OF
THE ROYAL SCHOOOLS OF MUSIC

SWINGING RHYMES

Three Blue Mice

TERENCE GREAVES

Steady, with a firm beat ♩ = c.120

AB 2273

Baa, Baa, Blue Sheep

In strict time ♩ = c. 96

Little Blue Peep and Little Boy Blue

Little Blue Jug

Nutty Little Blue Tree

Oh, the Blue Old Duke of York

Polly, Rock the Kettle on

Lavender's Blue Rock Waltz

una corda

tre corde

molto rall.

Lento

* ossia: ♩ ♩ ♩ | in L.H.

Waltz – Latin – Rock a'Bye Baby

Bonny Bobby Bluetoe

AB 2273

Reproduced and printed by
Halstan & Co. Ltd., Amersham, Bucks., England